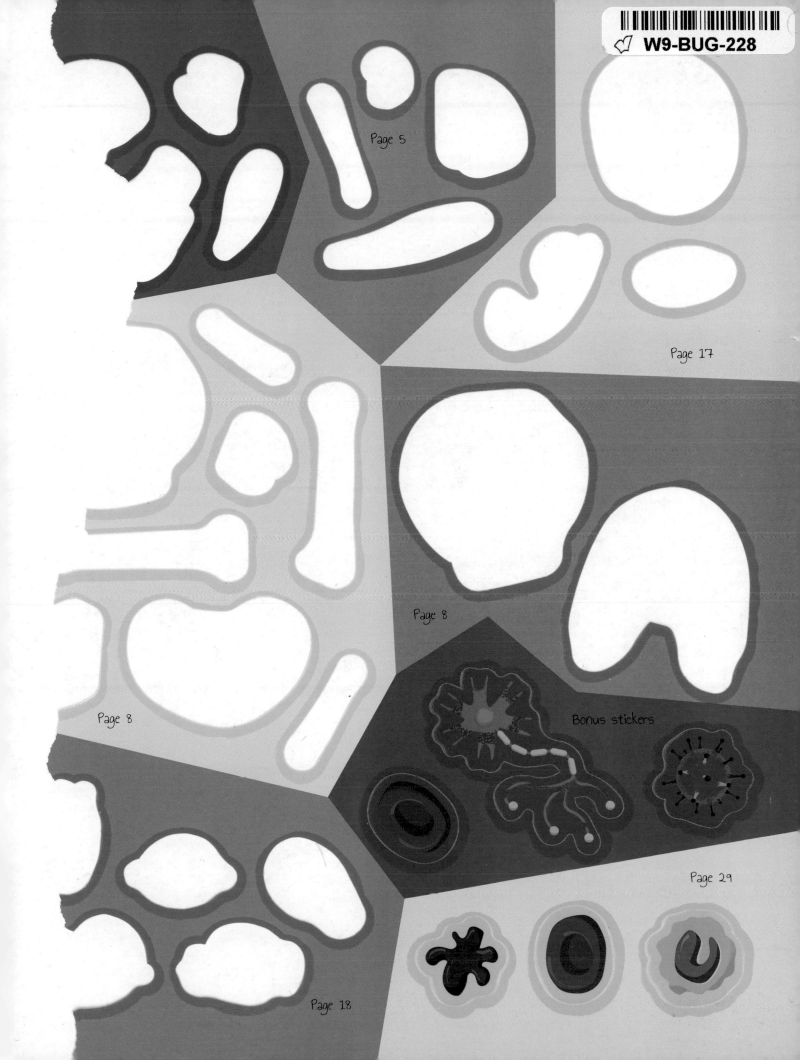

W9-BUG-228

Page 5

Page 17

Page 8

Page 8

Bonus stickers

Page 29

Page 18

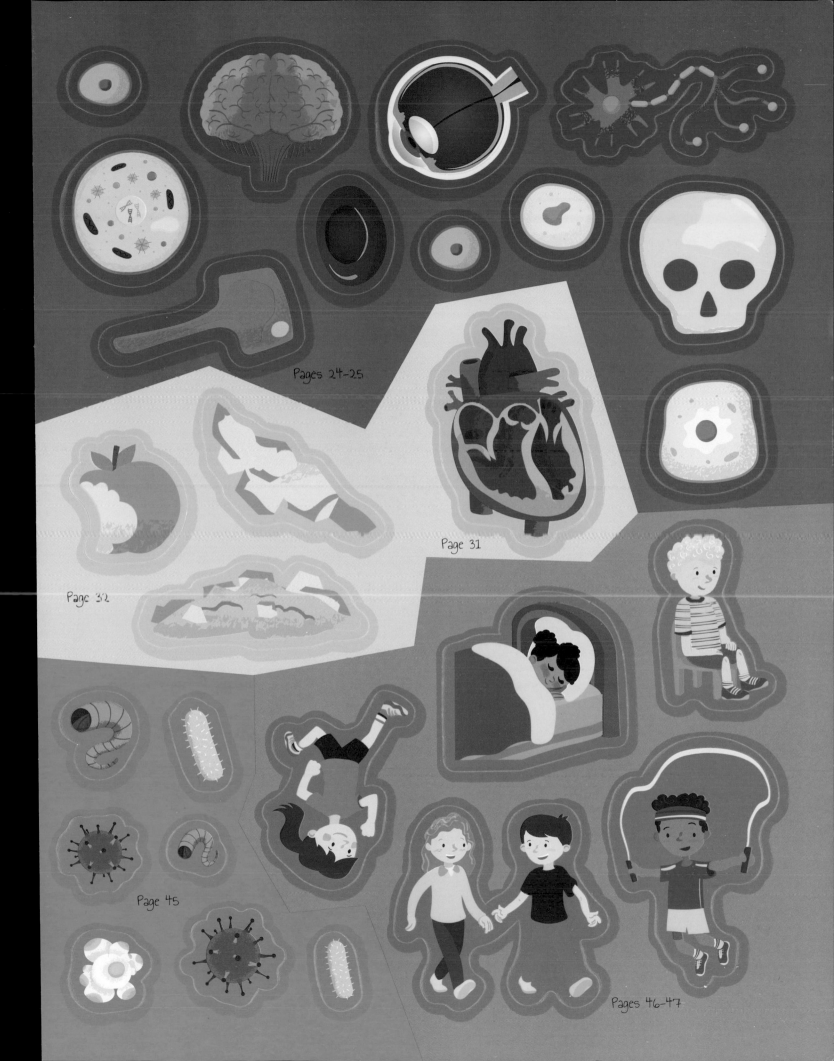

Pages 24-25

Page 31

Page 32

Page 45

Pages 46-47

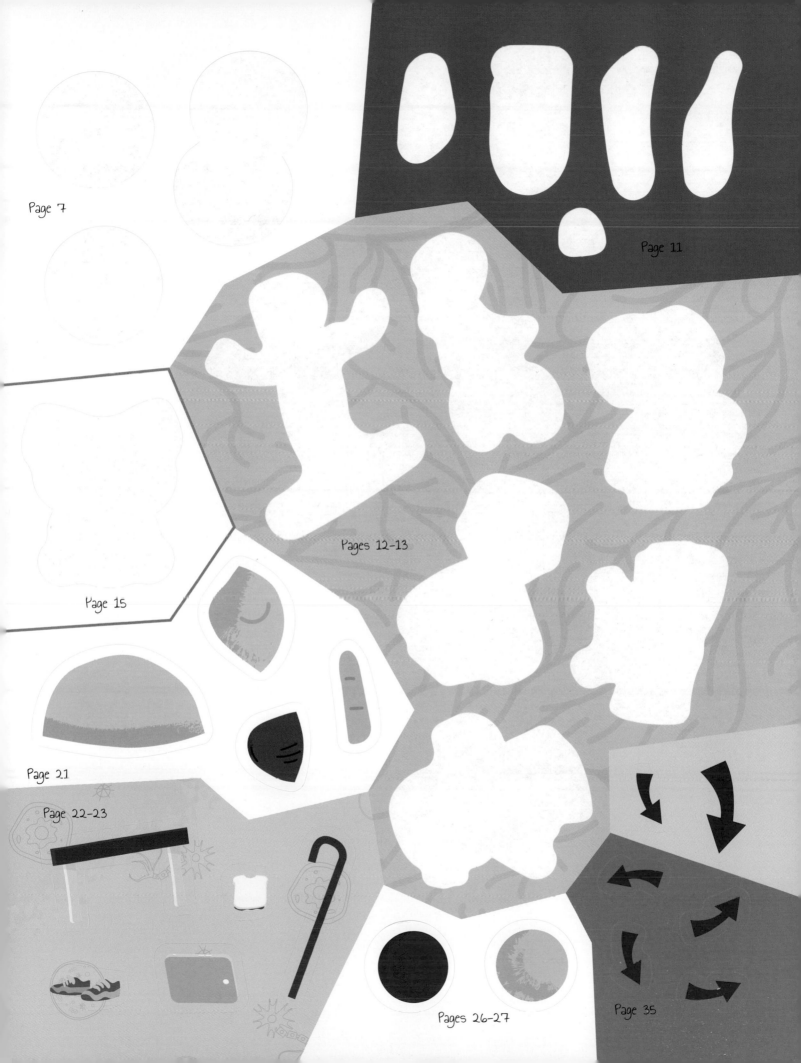

Page 7

Page 11

Pages 12-13

Page 15

Page 21

Page 22-23

Pages 26-27

Page 35

Page 37

Page 39

Page 41

Page 42

Bonus stickers

Page 48

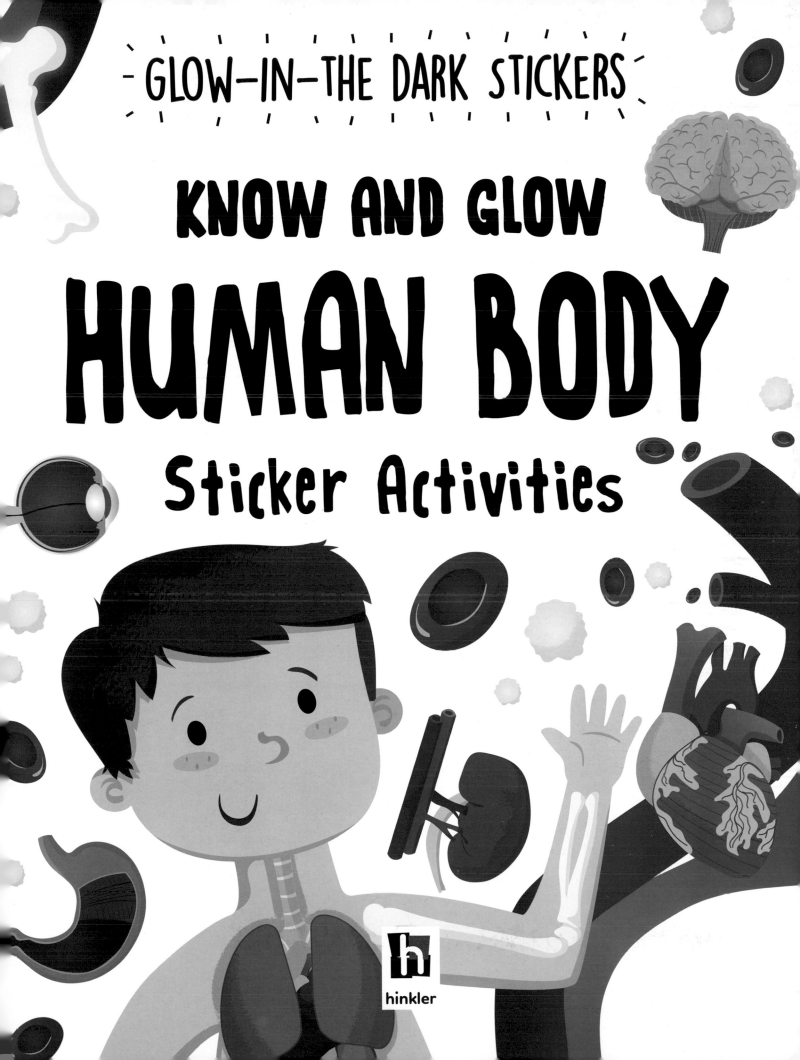

Published by Hinkler Pty Ltd
45–55 Fairchild Street
Heatherton Victoria 3202 Australia
www.hinkler.com

hinkler

© Hinkler Pty Ltd 2018, 2019

Packaged by Collaborate Agency

ISBN: 978 1 4889 4231 0

Printed and bound in Malaysia

CONTENTS

YOUR BODY

Your body is amazing. It's like a super-charged machine, with lots of separate parts that work together spectacularly so you can stand, move, see, hear, feel, and, most importantly, think! And just as a machine needs to be well looked after to perform at its best, your body also needs plenty of supplies (like oxygen, food, and water) and maintenance to keep doing all the fantastic things it does.

You're about to go on an incredible journey that will take you around and inside your body to discover what it's made up of, how it works, and what it needs.

FIND OUT...

✹ Which bone in your body is no bigger than a grain of rice?

✹ Where is the thickest skin on your body?

✹ What's the hardest-working muscle in your body?

✹ Why do you get goosebumps when you are scared?

✹ Which part of your body is strong enough to dissolve metal?

Add glow-in-the-dark stickers to show what's inside the body.

INSIDE AND OUTSIDE

Stand in front of a mirror and you can see your face, chest, arms, and legs. But what's inside your body? Your bones, organs, and layers of muscles. Networks of tiny blood vessels connect the different organs to each other. An adult has 206 bones, 22 organs, and over 600 muscles.

YOUR BONES

You have bones from the top of your head to the tip of your toe. You even have 14 bones in your face! Bones are the hardest parts of your body and vary a lot in size, from very big to really tiny. The longest bone is your thigh bone, called the **femur**, and the smallest bones, called the **ossicles**, are found in your ears.

YOUR ORGANS

Inside your body, you have groups of organs and body parts that work together in systems to help you to breathe, move, and grow. Your heart is part of your **circulatory system**, your brain is part of your **nervous system**, your lungs are part of your **respiratory system**, and your liver and pancreas are part of your **digestive system**.

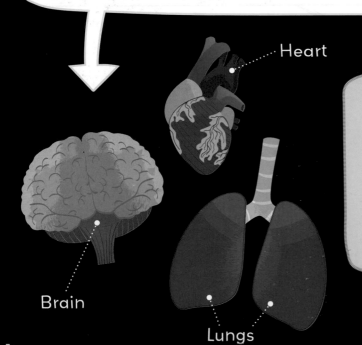

Heart

Brain

Lungs

YOUR MUSCLES

You have two types of muscles. Some muscles, like the ones in your arms and legs, help you to move. Other muscles, like the ones in your heart, help your body to work.

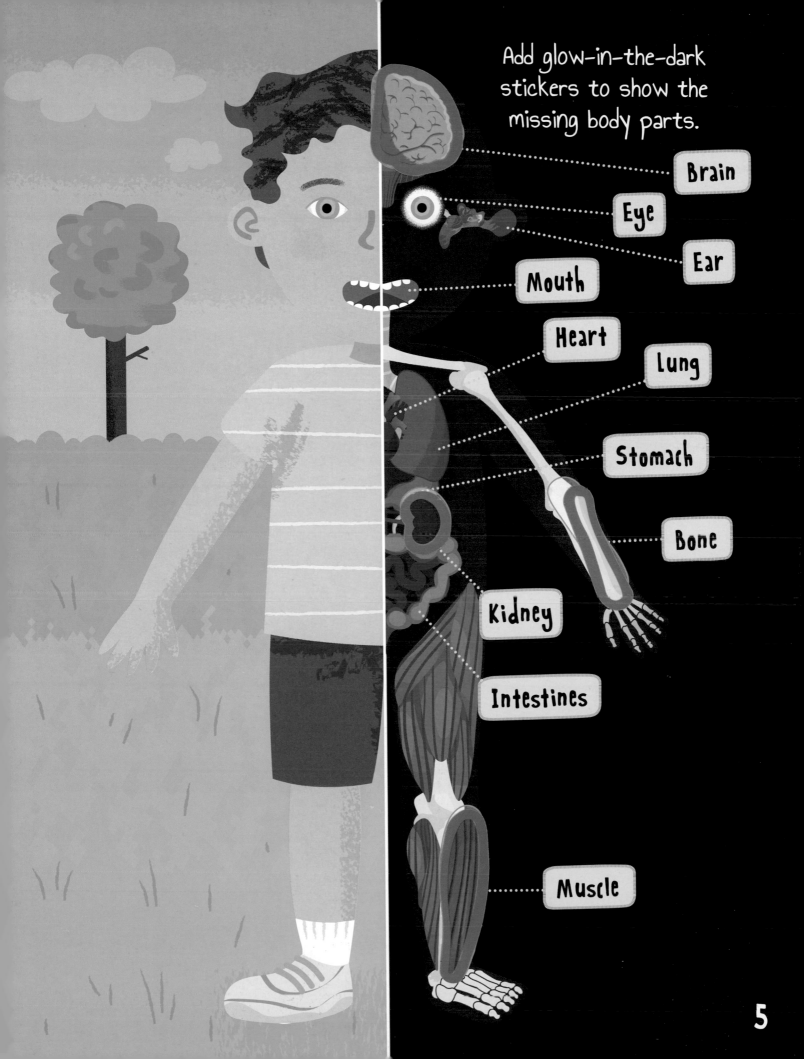

Add glow-in-the-dark stickers to show the missing body parts.

Brain

Eye

Ear

Mouth

Heart

Lung

Stomach

Bone

Kidney

Intestines

Muscle

BODY BUILDING BLOCKS

Everything in your body is made up of billions of cells, and they each have a specific job to do. Cells are the building blocks of every living thing, and they are so tiny that you can only see them through a **microscope** (an instrument used for viewing very small objects that magnifies them several hundred times). The cells in your body are constantly making more of themselves to keep you alive and healthy.

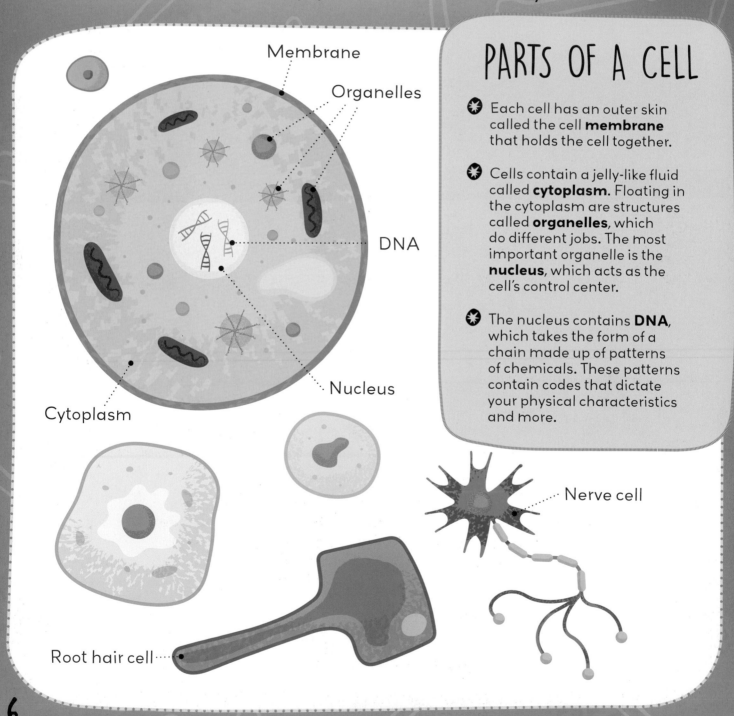

Membrane

Organelles

DNA

Nucleus

Cytoplasm

Root hair cell

Nerve cell

PARTS OF A CELL

✳ Each cell has an outer skin called the cell **membrane** that holds the cell together.

✳ Cells contain a jelly-like fluid called **cytoplasm**. Floating in the cytoplasm are structures called **organelles**, which do different jobs. The most important organelle is the **nucleus**, which acts as the cell's control center.

✳ The nucleus contains **DNA**, which takes the form of a chain made up of patterns of chemicals. These patterns contain codes that dictate your physical characteristics and more.

MAKING NEW CELLS

✦ To keep growing, your body has to create new cells. These new cells are formed when a cell divides into two. This process is called **mitosis**.

✦ The length of a cell's life can vary depending on its function—some muscle cells live for up to 15 years, while cells in your stomach last only 5 days before they are replaced with new ones!

Complete the stages of mitosis by adding the missing stickers.

Stage 1: The process starts with a single cell.

Stage 3: The X shapes line up in preparation to separate.

Stage 5: The cells split to make two new cells.

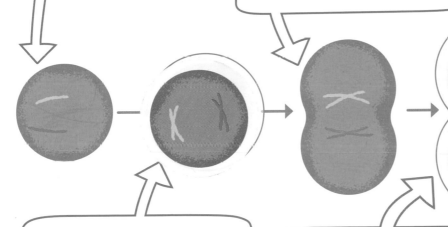

Stage 2: Each strand of DNA doubles itself, making an X shape.

Stage 4: The X shapes separate into 2 sets of DNA, and the cells start to divide.

DIFFERENT TYPES OF CELL

The different types of cells in your body all have unique and important jobs to do. For example, red blood cells deliver oxygen around your body, while white blood cells protect you from disease.

Red blood cell

White blood cells

STAND UP!

Your skeleton provides a frame for your body, to hold it up and prevent you from collapsing on the floor! Your bones are stronger than concrete, so they're perfect for protecting your internal organs, as well. You are born with about 300 bones, but some of these fuse together as you grow, leaving you with 206.

THE BARE BONES

✱ The bones in your skeleton can be divided into five main groups: your skull, your spine, your rib cage, your pelvis bones, and the bones in your arms and legs.

✱ You have 27 bones in each hand and 26 bones in each foot!

✱ Some bones protect soft parts of your body. Your skull protects your brain and your ribcage protects your heart and lungs.

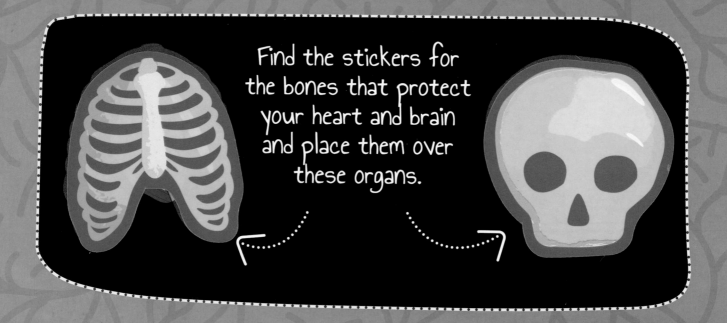

Find the stickers for the bones that protect your heart and brain and place them over these organs.

JOINTS

Your joints connect your bones and help them to move. You have two types of joints:

✱ **A hinge joint** allows the bones to move easily in one direction. Try bending your knee and you'll see it only goes one way—it's a hinge joint. Pushing against the hinge is often uncomfortable, but double-jointed people can bend their bones in both directions!

✱ **A ball-and-socket joint** allows a bone to move backwards and forwards, up and down, and in a circular motion. There's a ball-and-socket joint between your shoulder and your upper arm. See how many directions you can move your arm!

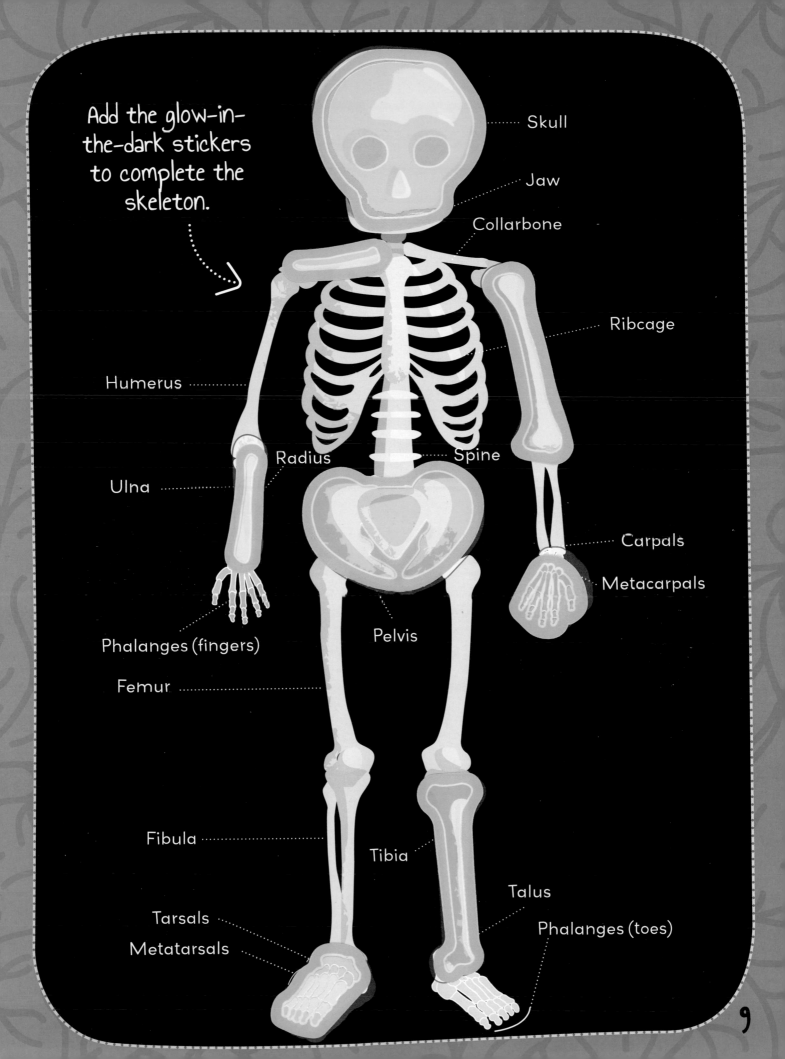

Add the glow-in-the-dark stickers to complete the skeleton.

Skull

Jaw

Collarbone

Ribcage

Humerus

Radius

Spine

Ulna

Carpals

Metacarpals

Phalanges (fingers)

Pelvis

Femur

Fibula

Tibia

Talus

Tarsals

Phalanges (toes)

Metatarsals

9

KEEP MOVING!

Muscles are like chunky bundles of elastic bands and are made up of thousands of small fibers. Many muscles help your bones to move. These are called **skeletal muscles.** You also have heart muscles as well as muscles in organs like your eyes, stomach, and bladder. Your bladder muscles allow you to hold on to your pee until you can get to a toilet!

HOW A SKELETAL MUSCLE WORKS

Skeletal muscles work in pairs: one on the top of the two bones they're attached to, and one underneath. When you bring the two bones closer to each other—like when you bend your arm—the muscle on top shortens and the muscle underneath lengthens at the same time.

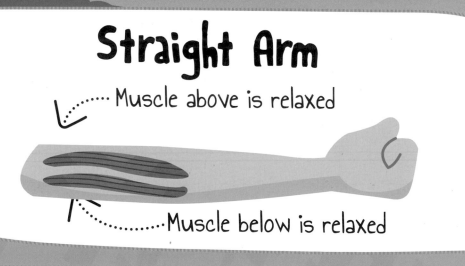

Straight Arm

Muscle above is relaxed

Muscle below is relaxed

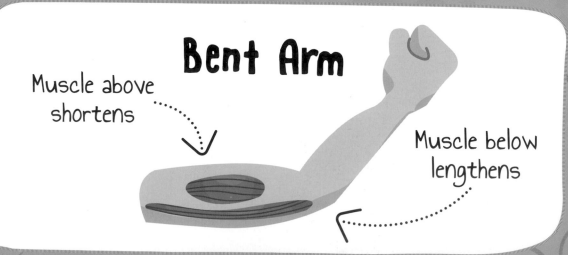

Bent Arm

Muscle above shortens

Muscle below lengthens

Add the stickers for the missing muscles.

Nasalis
Opens and closes your nostrils, helping you to breathe.

Bicep
Bends your arms.

Abdominal muscles
Moves the torso and helps breathing.

Thigh muscles
Moves your legs and hips.

Calf muscles
Bends your legs and points your toes.

BUSY MUSCLES

✳ Some muscles work automatically, like the muscles in your stomach and intestines that push food through each organ. The muscles in your heart also work automatically all the time, making your heart beat to pump blood around your body.

✳ There are more than 40 muscles in your face that help you to laugh, frown, and even to wrinkle your nose!

THINK!

Your brain is brilliant! It controls nearly everything that goes on in your body. It also tells you how to respond to the outside world. Your brain thinks about all the information it receives, decides how your body should react, and then memorizes it for the future. Amazing!

BRAINY FACTS

✹ Your brain is about the size of two clenched fists, but it is also full of folds so that it holds as much information as possible. If all the folds were ironed out, it would be about the size of a pillowcase.

✹ While your brain is only 2 percent of the size of your body, it uses about 20 percent of your body's energy. This shows how busy it is!

✹ Your brain has a staggering 100 billion nerve cells!

Using apps

Cerebrum

Jumping away from a spider

SUPER BRAIN

Your brain is constantly working. It thinks, orders, actions, and controls muscles. There is a particular part of the brain for each of these jobs.

1. The **CEREBRUM** is the largest part of the brain. It plays an important role in the way we speak, hear, see, move, and remember things. It also processes sensory information such as touch, temperature, and pain. But most importantly, this is where all your thinking happens. Your cerebrum is involved whenever you solve a puzzle, use an app, or decide who to play with.

2. The **CEREBELLUM** controls your body's movement, coordination, and balance. This is the part of the brain that takes charge when you rollerblade or walk across a balancing beam.

Find stickers for each part of the brain which demonstrate activities for which that part is largely responsible.

Reading

Cycling

Walking on a balance beam

Cerebellum

Reacting to an ice-cream headache

Brain stem

3. The **BRAIN STEM** connects your brain to your nervous system. Nerves run from the brain stem, down your spine, branching out and sending messages to every part of your body. Your brain stem controls important functions that you don't consciously need to think about, such as your heart beating and your breathing. It determines whether you feel sleepy or wide awake, allows you to quickly move away from something dangerous, and it also controls your reflexes. So if you touch a hotplate, your brain stem sends an instruction to pull your hand away fast!

13

LOOK!

Your eyes do an incredible job. Have a look around you—you can see and make sense of everything because your eyes are constantly taking in all those different colors and shapes, nearby and far away, and sending that information to your brain to be processed.

HOW WE SEE

✺ The **iris** is the colored part of your eye. In the middle of the iris is a small, black, circular opening called the **pupil**, which allows light rays to enter your eye. The iris changes the size of the pupil, making it bigger to let in more light, and smaller to let in less light.

✺ Just behind the iris sits a clear, flexible **lens**. Its job is to sharpen the light rays on the **retina** at the back of the eyeball. The image of what you are looking at appears upside down on your retina.

✺ The image is then sent from the retina along the **optic nerve** to the brain. The brain cleverly turns the image the right way up again for you to process what you are seeing.

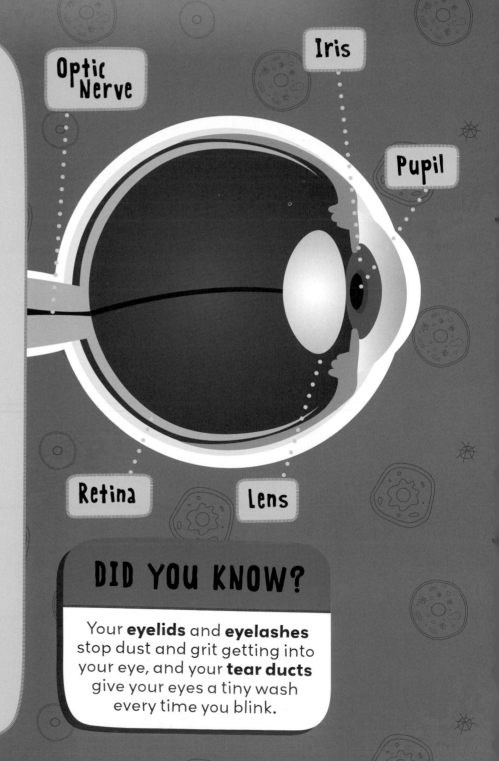

Optic Nerve

Iris

Pupil

Retina

Lens

DID YOU KNOW?

Your **eyelids** and **eyelashes** stop dust and grit getting into your eye, and your **tear ducts** give your eyes a tiny wash every time you blink.

Complete the sequence of how you "see" something by adding the missing sticker.

...... Now, draw the teddy the final way you see it.

YOUR EYES AND BRAIN

Your eyes send a constant stream of pictures to your brain, which then decides how to respond. So, if your optic nerve sends your brain a picture of a delicious ice-cream cone, your brain tells your tongue to start salivating!

FUN EYE FACTS

✸ You blink about 12 times every minute.

✸ The tiny muscles that are responsible for moving and adjusting your eyes are the most active muscles in your body. If you sit down to read a book for an hour, these muscles will make nearly 10,000 movements!

✸ Newborn babies may cry, but they can't produce any tears for at least one month.

Answers: The teddy should be drawn the right way up.

LISTEN!

Another important sense that you have is hearing. You may think that you know what your ears look like, but that's just the **outer ear.** Behind the outer ear, inside your head, are the **middle ear** and the **inner ear.** Sound is collected by the outer ear, travels through the middle and inner ear, and then sent—yes, you guessed it—to the brain!

HOW WE HEAR

✸ The fleshy flap on each side of your head is called the **pinna** or **auricle**, and it's designed to collect sound waves. These sound waves are sent along a narrow tube called the **ear canal** to the middle ear.

✸ In the middle ear, sound waves are turned into vibrations by the **eardrum**, which is a thin piece of skin stretched tightly across your ear canal, like a drum. The sound waves cause the tight skin of the eardrum to vibrate.

✸ When the eardrum vibrates, it moves three tiny bones called the **ossicles**, which help the vibrations travel into the inner ear.

✸ Finally, the vibrations reach the inner ear and enter a small, coiled tube called the **cochlea.** The cochlea is filled with liquid, which moves like a wave when the ossicles vibrate. These waves disturb the tiny hairs that cover the cochlea. When the hairs detect this movement, they create special nerve signals.

✸ The nerve signals are sent to the brain, which decodes them and understands them as a particular sound.

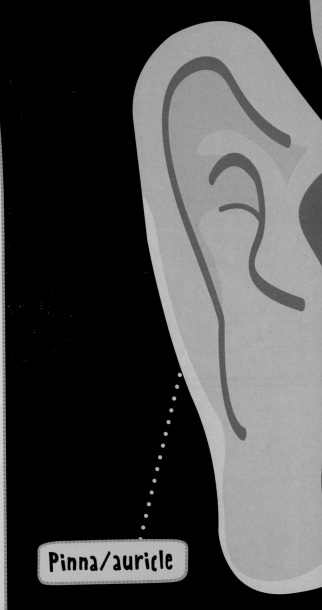

Pinna/auricle

Place the correct glow-in-the-dark stickers over the missing parts of the ear below.

Ossicles

Cochlea

KEEPING YOUR BALANCE

✱ Your ears don't just collect sounds; they have another important job. They help to keep you balanced. The liquid in your cochlea lets your brain know when you are moving. The brain then makes sure all your muscles are working properly so you don't fall over.

Eardrum

Ear canal

FUN EAR FACTS

✱ The ossicles are the smallest bones in your body. The tiniest bone is called the **stirrup** and is around the size of a grain of rice.

✱ Your ears often "pop" when the air outside your ear pushes against your eardrums, like when you are taking off on a plane or in a high-speed elevator. This is because the inside of your ear is connected to your nose and throat by a short tube (**eustachian tube**) that opens to make sure the air pressure is the same on both sides of your eardrum. When it opens, your ears pop.

✱ Dogs can hear something from four times farther away than the average person can.

DID YOU KNOW?

Earwax might look yucky but it keeps your ears healthy by protecting them from dirt and infection.

TASTE AND SMELL

Everyone knows that your mouth helps you taste something and your nose helps you smell something. But did you know it's only when the taste or smell reaches your brain that you decide whether you like it or not? If you don't, your brain might tell you to spit out the bad-tasting food—or to hold your nose!

YOUR SENSE OF TASTE

✴ Poke your tongue out and you will see tiny pink lumps called **papillae** on the surface. Most of these contain **taste buds**, which are tiny sensory organs. When you eat something, these taste buds use **microscopic** (so small that you can only see them with a microscope) hairs to detect what type of taste the food has and sends these messages to the brain to interpret.

✴ There are five basic flavors: sweet, sour, bitter, salty, and umami (savory).

Bitter

Umami

Sour

Lemon

Sweet

Salty

Find a glow-in-the-dark food sticker to match each taste.

10 BASIC SMELLS

There are 10 basic smells. Smells that aren't on this list are actually a combination of two or more of these 10!

Toasted or nutty

Minty

Fragrant

Citrus

Woody

Fruity

Pungent (very strong)

Chemical

Sweet

Decayed

Draw arrows to show the direction of the smell moving from the nostrils all the way up to the brain

Brain

Cilia

Nostril

HOW YOU SMELL

✳ Your nose has two holes called **nostrils**. These draw air deep into your nose when you breathe in. They also draw in tiny "smell molecules" that are mixed together with that air.

✳ These smell molecules are sensed by tiny little hairs at the top of the inside of your nose. These are called **cilia**.

✳ The hairs send the information gathered about the smell to the brain, which decides whether you should find it pleasant or pongy!

TOUCH

Have you ever wondered how you know something feels hot? This is just one of the many clever things your skin can help to detect. Skin is an organ that works with the brain to provide you with your sense of touch. It tells you what things feel like, it controls your body temperature, and lets you know when you have been hurt. And, of course, skin holds your whole body together!

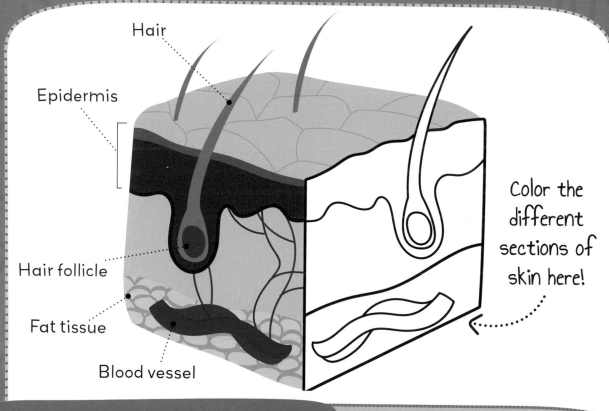

Hair

Epidermis

Hair follicle

Fat tissue

Blood vessel

Color the different sections of skin here!

HOW YOUR SKIN WORKS

✺ Your skin has millions of tiny nerve endings just below the surface. These nerve endings sense how something feels when you touch it—is it hot or cold, hard or soft, bumpy or smooth?

✺ The nerve endings then send this information to the brain, which gives instructions for how to respond. For example, if your hand touches an overly hot mug, the nerve endings send a pain message to the brain, which then tells your hand to pull away quickly from the mug.

Check the description of each type of skin and insert the right stickers to complete the pictures.

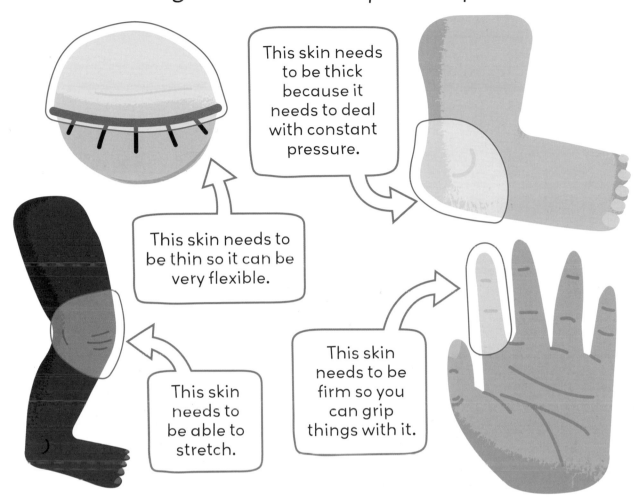

This skin needs to be thick because it needs to deal with constant pressure.

This skin needs to be thin so it can be very flexible.

This skin needs to be able to stretch.

This skin needs to be firm so you can grip things with it.

FUN SKIN FACTS

✸ Your skin is the biggest organ in your body.

✸ Your skin constantly renews itself, shedding 30,000 to 40,000 dead skin cells every minute.

✸ The thickest skin is on your heels and the thinnest skin is on your eyelids.

✸ Each hair on your body grows out of a tiny tube in the skin called a **follicle**. When you are cold or frightened, the hairs stand up—this is what causes goosebumps.

✸ Skin is covered by a special oil called **sebum**, which comes out of your sebaceous glands and keeps your skin moist and waterproof. If you stay too long in the bath or the pool, the water will wash away the sebum, and your skin will wrinkle. But don't worry, the oil soon comes back!

GROW UP!

The moment you were born, your bones, muscles, organs, and senses were all there and functioning. But there was so much your body still had to develop! During your first two years you mastered walking, talking, and eating solid food. Every year, your body continues to change but the amazing changes it went through in the first four years were greater than any other changes you will experience over the whole of your lifetime.

Add stickers to complete the pictures.

Eating solid food   Good physical skills

Growth spurt

KEY DEVELOPMENT STAGES

✸ At the age of two, you are around five times heavier and twice as tall as you were at birth.

✸ By the time you are five, your brain is the same size as an adult's and you are rapidly developing physical skills, such as jumping and running, and developing fine motor skills, such as writing and drawing.

✸ You continue to grow steadily until you are between 11 and 13 years old. Then you have a sudden growth spurt, which can be as much as 12 in (30 cm) in just one year. Boys have their growth spurt later than girls, but by around the age of 16, both will be close to their adult height.

AMAZING BABY FACTS

✹ For about the first twelve weeks, babies can only see in black and white and shades of gray because the nerve cells in their retinas are not fully developed.

✹ A healthy baby is born with 100 billion nerve cells in the brain—that's nearly twice as many as an adult, even though a baby's brain is half the size.

✹ As a result of all the rapid brain development, 60 percent of a baby's energy is spent on its brain, compared with 25 percent of an adult's energy.

Brain at its peak

Draw yourself as an adult!

Signs of ageing

✹ Between the ages of 18 and 20, your body largely stops growing. Over the next ten years, you are at your height of fitness and your brain is at its peak.

✹ As you grow older, your body takes longer to repair itself. When you are over the age of 60, your brain begins to shrink and signs of ageing (such as gray hair, wrinkles, and impaired hearing) become more obvious. A good diet and regular exercise throughout life can help keep muscles, joints, and bones stronger, and reduce the effects of ageing.

23

BODY QUIZ

Give yourself glow-in-the-dark reward stickers for completing the quiz!

Now you have seen all the amazing things your body can do, let's see how much you have remembered.

I. YOUR BONES

Your bones are as strong as... wood, plastic, or concrete?

....

2. YOUR BRAIN

What is the name of the largest part of your brain?

....

3. YOUR MUSCLES

The only part of your body that doesn't have muscles is your face. True or false?

TRUE ....☐

FALSE ....☐

4. YOUR EYES

What is the name of the small hole in the middle of your eye that lets light through?

....

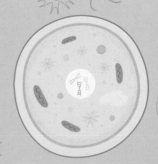

5. YOUR TONGUE

What is the name of the tiny pink bumps on your tongue that contain taste buds?

....

6. YOUR EARS

The inside of your ear contains very small bones that help to pass the sound along. True or false?

TRUE .... ☐

FALSE .... ☐

7. YOUR SKIN

Where is your skin the thickest?

....

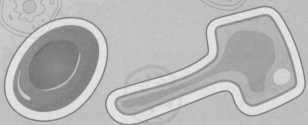

8. YOUR GROWTH

At what age does your body tend to stop growing?

....

Answers: 1. Concrete, 2. Cerebrum, 3. False, 4. Pupil, 5. Papillae, 6. True, 7. On your heels, 8. 18–20.

Now check the answers and see how you did!

I got 7–8 questions right.

Brilliant! Keep this up and you could be a doctor one day!

I got 4–6 questions right.

Great job! Maybe have another look at those tricky questions.

I got 0–3 questions right.

Bad luck! Have another read through all those amazing facts and you'll do much better next time.

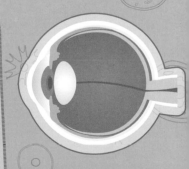

DEEP BREHTH!

Have you ever wondered what keeps your amazing body going? It's three simple things—air (the key element of which is known as **oxygen [O_2]**), food, and water. How does the oxygen in the air around you get inside your body? Well, that's the job of your lungs. If you put your hand on your chest and take a deep breath in and then breathe out again, you can feel your lungs working.

BREATHING IN

When you breathe in, different parts of your body work together.

✺ The muscle beneath your lungs (called the **diaphragm**) flattens and your ribs move up, creating space for your lungs to get bigger.

✺ You take in air through your nose and mouth. It travels down your **windpipe** (or **trachea**) and into your chest. Here the windpipe divides into two smaller tubes, each called a **bronchus**. One leads into your left lung and one into your right lung.

✺ Inside your lungs, the tubes keep branching like a tree into thinner and thinner tubes called **bronchioles**. At the end of each bronchiole are millions of tiny air bubbles called **alveoli**.

✺ Oxygen passes through the thin walls of the **alveoli** into tiny blood vessels called **capillaries**.

✺ The journey doesn't stop there: oxygen is then carried by the blood, providing energy to all the cells in your body.

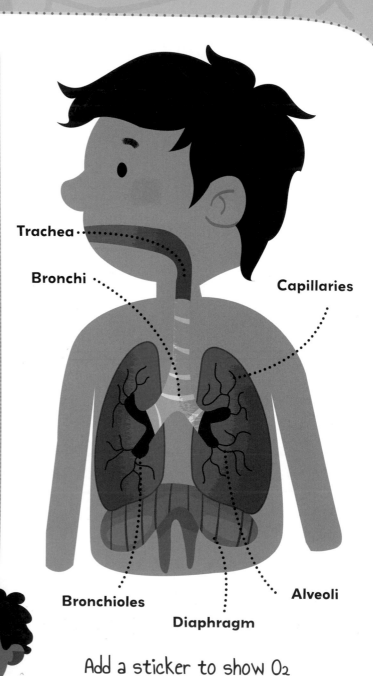

Trachea

Bronchi

Capillaries

Bronchioles

Diaphragm

Alveoli

O_2

Add a sticker to show O_2 being breathed in.

Add a sticker to show CO_2 being breathed out.

CO_2

BREATHING OUT

When your cells have taken out the oxygen, what's left in the blood is a waste gas called **carbon dioxide (CO_2)**, which your body needs to get rid of. When you breathe out, your diaphragm relaxes and moves up, pushing the carbon dioxide out of your lungs, up your trachea, and out through your nose and mouth.

Which of these characters is the odd one out? Color them in!

A

B

C

D

Answer: D is the odd one out because she is sipping a drink in, while the others are breathing air out.

FUN LUNG FACTS

✳ The lung on the left side of your body is smaller than the lung on the right side because the left lung shares space in the left side of the chest with the heart.

✳ Tiny hairs (called **cilia**) in your trachea stop dirt getting into your lungs.

✳ Each lung has about 30,000 tiny bronchioles. If you joined them all together, they would stretch for over 3,200 km (2,000 miles).

BLOOD

Your blood is like a super-fast underground train that carries oxygen and **nutrients** (substances that nourish your body) around your body. On its journey, it travels through blood vessels that branch out to reach every part of your body.

Do you know what blood type you are?

BLOOD TYPES

If you ever require more blood, doctors need to know your blood type, so they can match it correctly. Depending on the proteins found in your red blood cells, your blood is described as either A, B, or O. If your blood contains the Rh protein, your blood is positive and if it doesn't, then it's negative. Either way, it's fine!

WHAT'S INSIDE YOUR BLOOD?

When you have a cut, you can see your blood, but what you can't see is what's inside that blood. Blood is made up of four parts, each of which has a special job:

✱ **Red blood cells** carry oxygen around your body. They also contain a protein (nutrient) called **hemoglobin**, which contains iron to keep you healthy.

✱ **White blood cells** fight infection. When you are sick, your body makes more white blood cells to fight your illness.

✱ **Platelets** are cells that stop a cut from bleeding too much. Platelets stick together to form a blood clot. As the clot dries out, it forms a scab.

✱ **Plasma** is a yellowish liquid that carries proteins and nutrients around your body. It also carries **hormones** (chemicals that instruct your body cells what to do), like the growth hormone that tells your bones and muscles to grow.

Use glow-in-the-dark stickers to add the different types of blood cell to this blood vessel.

Red blood cell

White blood cell

Platelet

DID YOU KNOW?

Scabs may look yucky but they protect you from infection. They are a tough crust that forms over a cut or wound that stops germs getting inside. This gives the skin cells underneath a chance to heal.

FUN FACTS

✺ Your blood travels about 19,000 km (12,000 miles) in just one day.

✺ All the blood in your body would fill about 3 whole 34-oz (1-liter) bottles.

✺ Hemoglobin gives your blood its red color. Blood isn't always red—a worm has green blood and an octopus has blue blood!

THUMP! THUMP!

Although it is only the size of your fist, your heart is a very strong pump. It sends about 100 oz (3 liters) of blood around your body every single minute! When you feel your heart beating, you are feeling it quickly contracting and expanding.

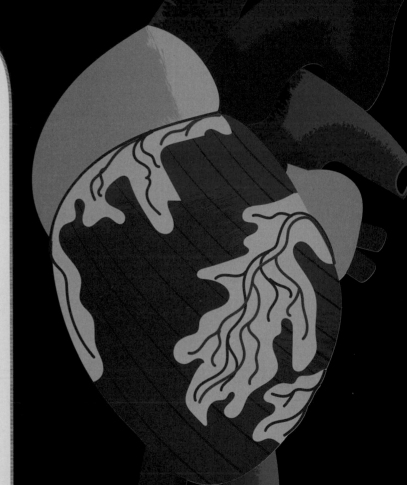

HOW YOUR HEART WORKS

Your heart's job is to make sure all the good things in your blood reach every part of your body. So, when the blood containing oxygen leaves your lungs, a large blood vessel takes it to your heart, which then pumps it around your body. Your blood leaves your heart through blood vessels called **arteries**, which have thick muscular walls to help forcefully push the blood along.

When your body has used up all the oxygen in your blood, blood vessels called **veins** take that blood back to your heart. Veins have thinner walls than arteries, as the blood returning to your heart does not need to be pushed as hard. Because this blood now has lots of waste instead of oxygen, your heart pumps it back to your lungs, where the waste is removed when you breathe out.

Add a glow-in-the-dark
heart sticker here!

Aorta

Superior vena
cava

Pulmonary
artery

Pulmonary
vein

Left atrium

Right
atrium

Aortic valve

Pulmonary
valve

Left
ventricle

Tricuspid
valve

Inferior vena
cava (vein)

Right
ventricle

HEARTY FACTS

✿ During your life, your heart will beat over 3 billion times!

✿ You can feel your heartbeat in certain blood vessels when you take your pulse.
Try placing two fingers over the artery in your wrist or at the side of your neck.

✿ It takes just 16 seconds for your heart to pump blood down to your toes and for
that blood to come back to your heart.

✿ Your heart works harder than any other muscle in your body.

MOUTH-WATERING!

Just as your body needs oxygen, it also needs food, both of which provide energy to keep you going. But how does food reach the various parts of your body? It goes through a long process known as **digestion**. This food journey starts the moment you pop food into your mouth.

PREPARING THE FOOD

Food needs to be broken into smaller pieces, so you can swallow it. Your sharp-edged front teeth, called **incisors**, cut off pieces of the food. Then your blunt, strong back teeth, called **molars**, grind it down. As you are chewing, your mouth releases a special fluid called **saliva**—also known as spit! With the help of your tongue, the saliva mixes with the food to break it down even more.

Use your glow-in-the-dark stickers to show what happens to food in your mouth as you are eating.

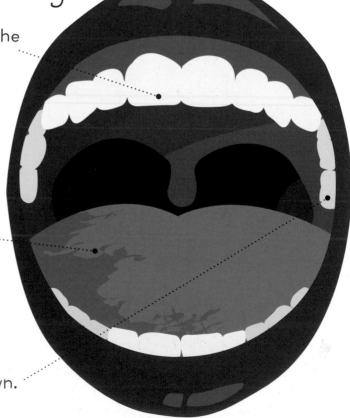

Incisor teeth break the food off in chunks.

The tongue tastes the food.

Molar teeth grind the food down.

DID YOU KNOW?

Your mouth produces about 30 oz (1 liter) of saliva every day!

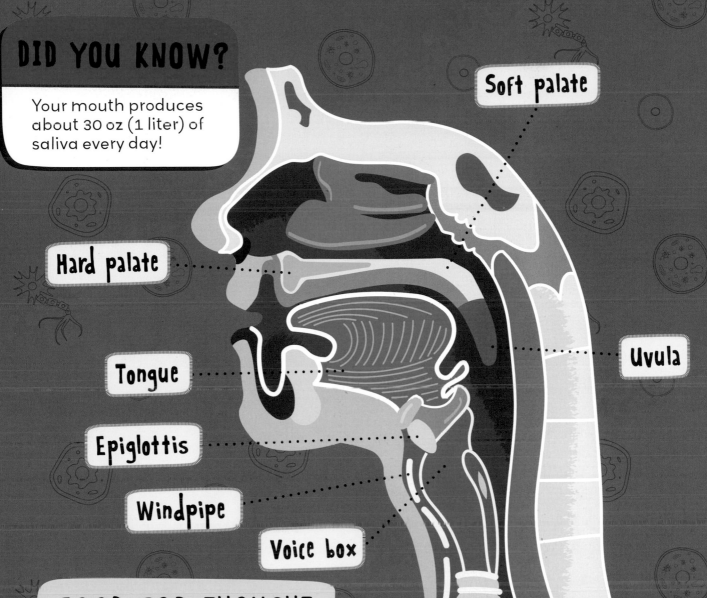

Soft palate

Hard palate

Tongue

Epiglottis

Windpipe

Voice box

Uvula

FOOD FOR THOUGHT

When you swallow food, how can you be sure it will go down to your stomach and not up the nasal passages at the back of your throat to your nose?

Answer: If you open your mouth and look in the mirror, you will see a sort of small flexible "finger" hanging down at the back of your throat. This is called your **uvula.** As you swallow, the back of your tongue presses the uvula against your nasal passages to close them off.

How can you be sure the food goes down the tube to your stomach, rather than down your windpipe?

Answer: You can't see this one, but at the back of your throat there is a small flap between your windpipe and the tube that goes down to your stomach. This is called your **epiglottis.** When you swallow, the epiglottis covers the windpipe, to prevent food from entering it and making you choke.

STOMACH CHURNING!

The second stage of the food journey takes place in your stomach. This is a large muscular "sack," part way down your digestive tubes. The food mashed up by your teeth, tongue, and saliva passes down into your stomach through a long tube called the **esophagus**. The stomach then acts like a washing machine, churning the food and making it even mushier.

WHAT YOUR STOMACH DOES

✳ Using its strong muscular walls, your stomach starts to churn the food.

✳ The stomach walls produce very acidic juices that help to break down the food even more. It's just like adding detergent to a washing-machine cycle.

✳ By the time your stomach has finished its work, the food is now more like a soup. A valve at the bottom of the stomach opens and the food passes down into the next stage of your food journey: the small intestine.

DID YOU KNOW?

Most people think your stomach is somewhere behind your bellybutton. But it's quite a lot higher up; it's in your upper abdomen and is protected by your lower rib cage.

Join the dots to reveal the stomach.

34

FUN FACTS

✷ When you blush, your face turns red. But did you know that your stomach turns red too! It's because your body releases adrenaline when you're stressed, and this causes more blood to rush to different parts of your body, including your face and stomach, which makes them appear red.

✷ Burps are caused by swallowing small amounts of air with your food or drink. When you drink a fizzy drink, the bubbles contain a gas called carbon dioxide. Your stomach burps to get rid of this gas!

1. Muscular stomach walls help to churn the food

Add arrow stickers to show food traveling through the stomach.

3. The valve opens to let broken-down food into the small intestine

2. Acidic juices help to break down the food

ROUND AND ROUND!

The third and final stage of the food journey takes place in the **small intestine**: the long, coiled tube just below your stomach. This is where the most important part of the digestion process takes place. Here, the soup-like food passes into your blood so it can be sent all around your body to give you what you need.

In-test your skills! Make your way through the small intestine maze.

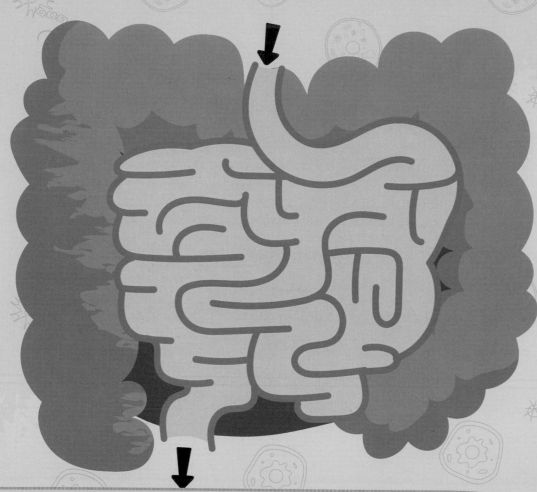

SUPER JUICE

❋ Special gastric juices from your **pancreas**, **liver**, and **gall bladder** (all organs) help to break down the soupy food in your small intestine, extracting the nutrients. Your pancreas makes juices that help you digest fats and proteins. Your liver produces a secretion called **bile** that helps absorb fats into your bloodstream. Your gall bladder stores that bile.

❋ Gastric juices are strong enough to dissolve metal!

FOOD JOURNEY THROUGH THE SMALL INTESTINE

Food comes in from the stomach

Sends nutrients to the brain

Sends nutrients to your organs

Sends nutrients to your bones

Sends nutrients to your muscles

Unwanted waste food

Pretend your pencil is food going through your small intestine. Start coloring at the entrance and go around and around to the exit, adding stickers as you go!

FUN FACTS

✺ If you stretched out all the small intestine of an adult, it would be longer than a large car (approximately 22 ft / 6.7 m).

✺ It's called the small intestine because of its width: it is only about the width of your middle finger (1.5 in / 4 cm).

✺ It can take up to four hours for the small intestine to separate your food into its nutrients, which then pass out through your blood vessels to the liver. Your liver helps to work out how many nutrients to keep and how many are sent around your body.

GET RID OF IT!

Your small intestine also deals with the parts of food that are not good for you. It sends this waste food down into a shorter but wider tube called your **large intestine** (the biggest part of which is known as the **colon**), which wraps around the outside of your small intestine. From now on, a more gross journey begins!

POO!

✹ The main job of your large intestine is to remove lots of the water from the waste food, so it is easier to remove it from your body.

✹ Waste food is slowly pushed through the thick, muscular tube of your large intestine. More and more water is removed during this journey, gradually making the waste more solid.

✹ By the time the waste food has reached the end of your large intestine, it has turned into the waste **poo**, which must leave your body.

GROSS FACT **1**

Sometimes, your large intestine might not remove enough water from your poo. This gives you **diarrhea**—liquid poo. If it removes too much water, the poo becomes hard, which gives you **constipation**, making it more difficult for you to push out your colon.

GROSS FACT **2**

Your poo can be stored inside your body for up to two days before you get rid of it.

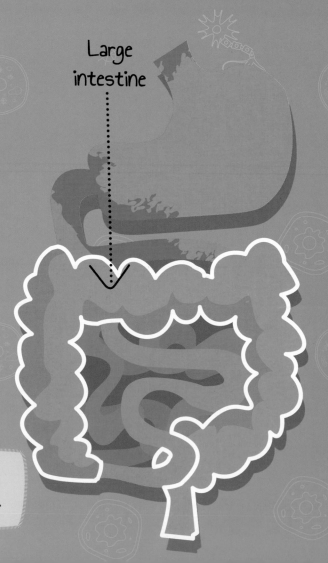

Large intestine

GROSS STICKERS!

Use the stickers to show the stages of your large intestine.

Gas builds up in the intestine, causing stinky farts!

Waste becomes darker and firmer as water is extracted from it

Waste food enters from small intestine

Waste now more solid (poo!), so it can pass out of the body

GROSS FACT 3

Farts are bubbles of smelly air that build up in the large intestine as the poo waits to be emptied. Everyone farts because it is important to get rid of this trapped air ... but try telling that to your friends standing nearby!

EAT HEALTHILY

How many times have you been told that vegetables are good for you and too much chocolate is bad for you? That's because some foods benefit your body, making you strong, helping you to perform well, and generally keeping you healthy, while some foods have less healthy or even unhealthy elements. It all depends on whether food contains plenty of nutrients.

Carbohydrates provide your body with energy.

Fats and oils are high in energy, and can be stored as fat on your body if you don't use the energy up!

Proteins help your cells grow and repair.

Minerals keep you healthy. The most important mineral is calcium, which keeps your bones and teeth strong.

Vitamins keep you healthy.

VITAMIN CHART

Vitamin	Examples of foods that contains vitamin	Benefits
A	VEGETABLES	GOOD FOR YOUR SKIN
B	BREAKFAST CEREALS	PROVIDES YOU WITH IRON
C	FRUIT AND VEGETABLES	PROTECTS AGAINST COLDS
D	EGGS AND FISH	HELPS BUILD STRONG BONES

FOODIE FACTS

✱ Foods containing lots of fiber are also very important, as they help to move your food easily along your large intestine. They act like a gentle scrubbing brush, cleaning your insides.

✱ Treats like chips, candies, and cookies are fine if they are eaten every so often, but their high amounts of fats and sugar (a type of carbohydrate) actually reduce rather than increase your energy and can cause other problems like storing excess fat.

Put your food stickers on the right plates.

For energy

For growth

For strong bones
and teeth

For good health

WHTER! WATER!

Oxygen and food are vital for your body, but there is also a third thing that your body needs: water. You need to drink plenty of water to stay healthy, but your body also has to get rid of a lot of it so you don't slosh around all day! Controlling your water level is the job of your **kidneys** and **bladder**.

WHY DO WE NEED WATER?

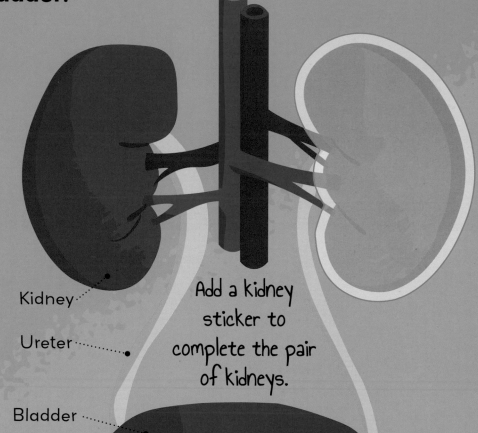

- ✱ Water provides a protective cushioning barrier for many of your organs and joints.

- ✱ Water helps to keep your body at the right temperature, which is why you should drink plenty of it if you have a fever.

Kidney

Ureter

Bladder

Add a kidney sticker to complete the pair of kidneys.

WHERE DOES YOUR PEE COME FROM?

- ✱ When you pee, you probably don't realize that this water has been on a long journey. The water started in your blood and picked up harmful toxins, making it waste.

- ✱ It was the job of your two kidneys to filter waste from the blood, which was carried by the water to produce urine (pee) to get rid of it from the body. If it had stayed in your body, you would have become ill.

- ✱ Your pee was then sent down a long thin tube to your bladder (called the **ureter**), which stored the pee until you were ready to go to the toilet.

AMAZING WATER FACTS

- ✪ Your blood is **83%** water.
- ✪ Your brain and muscles are **75%** water.
- ✪ Even your bones are **25%** water.

Copy and color the kidney.

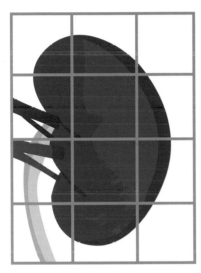

Water from body needing a clean

Water back to body after a clean

Waste toxin sent down to your bladder.

BODY DEFENDERS

There's a battle going on inside your body! Good things like oxygen, food, and water keep you healthy but there are also **germs** that can cause harm. Germs are microscopic living things that can invade your body and cause diseases. To defend against germs, some parts of your body work together to become your **immune system**.

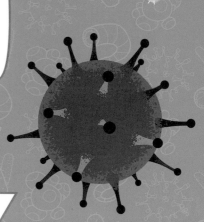

Bacteria are tiny organisms that live in your body, helping it to function properly. Some help make you healthy. Some bad bacteria, however, can also give your organs infections, like pneumonia that attacks your lungs.

Viruses are infectious agents that can only survive if they invade your body. They cause diseases like flu.

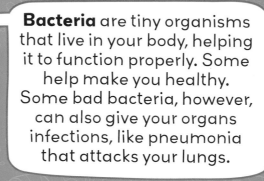

Fungi are small, plant-like organisms. Some fungi grow in the soil (like mushrooms), while some prefer other places, including your body! Fungi in your body cause problems like itchy rashes.

YOUR IMMUNE SYSTEM

- ✱ The **white cells** in your blood fight germs. Some of these cells kill the germs, while others store details about the types of germ that has invaded your body, so that your body is able to deal with it faster next time.

- ✱ Your **lymph glands** filter out germs that attack your body. These glands are in your neck, in your armpits, and behind your knee. Normally, you cannot feel them, but they swell up when they are defending your body against germs.

Parasites are creatures that feed off parts of your body and can make you sick. One type of parasite is a tapeworm, which lives in your stomach and eats your food.

Use your glow-in-the-dark stickers to add some germs to the toilet cloud!

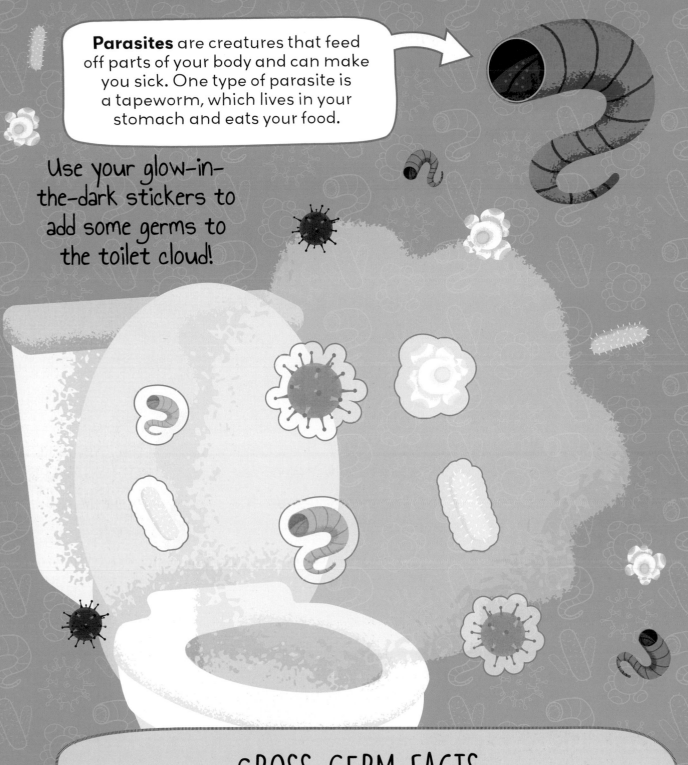

GROSS GERM FACTS

✹ When you flush the toilet, a cloud of germs shoots up 6.5 ft (2 m) high. So, in future, flush, then jump well back (or close the toilet seat...)!

✹ One of the areas in a school where you are most likely to pick up germs is on the bars of the climbing equipment in the playground.

✹ Automatic teller machines have millions of germs because of all the fingers touching them. They even have more germs than a public toilet.

STAYING HEALTHY

It is very important to look after your body. The best way to do this is to remind yourself of the three things that your body needs most: oxygen, food, and water. This means plenty of exercise, sensible eating, and drinking enough fluids. Exercise causes your heart to beat faster, sending lots of oxygen around your body. Also, remember all those germs you have to fight off; always try to practice careful hygiene as well!

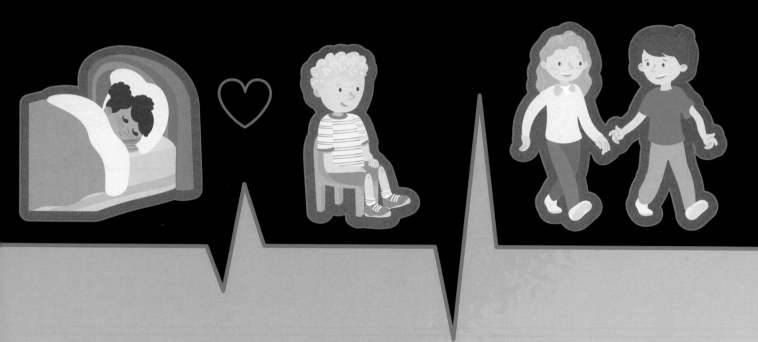

EXERCISE

Different exercises benefit different parts of your body. For instance, jumping rope and trampolining strengthen your bones and joints, while climbing on a climbing frame is good for your muscles. Exercises where you move quickly, like running and cycling, help your lungs and heart take in more oxygen. The more intense the exercise, the faster your heart needs to beat.

BRUSH YOUR TEETH

Once your baby teeth fall out and your adult teeth grow through, they are there for the rest of your life. This means that if they decay or fall out, they can only be replaced with false teeth. That's why it's important to brush your teeth twice a day, so you can keep them all.

Add glow-in-the-dark stickers to the activities below.
Going from left to right are activities that increasingly
make your heart beat faster!

Draw yourself doing
something that
makes your heart
beat faster!

PROTECTING YOUR HEALTH

✸ Thoroughly wash your hands regularly to avoid picking up any bacterial infections.

✸ To avoid getting a virus, turn away when friends sneeze or cough ... or insist they use a tissue!

✸ Dry between your toes properly and change those sweaty socks to prevent fungal rashes, like athlete's foot.

✸ Wash your hands before preparing food, and check that your food is properly cooked to avoid parasites and bacteria getting into your body and making you sick.

YUUR BODY QUIZ

Add reward stickers!

Can you remember the important things that your body needs to keep going? Having seen everything your body can do, now you know just how amazing it really is!

1. What gives your blood its red color?

✸ Bacteria

✸ Hemoglobin

✸ Vitamins

2. Your lungs are for breathing in oxygen. True or false?

TRUE .... ☐

FALSE .... ☐

3. What type of blood vessel carries blood from your heart?

✸ Vein   ✸ Capillary   ✸ Artery

....

4. How does drinking water help when you have a fever?

....

....

5. Put these three parts of the food journey through your body in the right order: stomach, small intestine, mouth.

....

....

6. Which nutrient helps your cells grow and repair themselves?

✸ protein   ✸ calcium

✸ vitamins   ✸ fats

....

I got 5–6 questions right.
WOW! Maybe you can skip that medical training!

I got 3–4 questions right.
You are well on your way to becoming a top doctor! Keep at it!

I got 0–2 questions right.
You are at the start of your training. After some more practice, try again and you'll do well!

Answers: 1. Hemoglobin; 2. True; 3. Artery; 4. It helps keep your body at the right temperature and prevents you from overheating; 5. mouth, stomach, small intestine; 6. protein.